P9-AZX-577

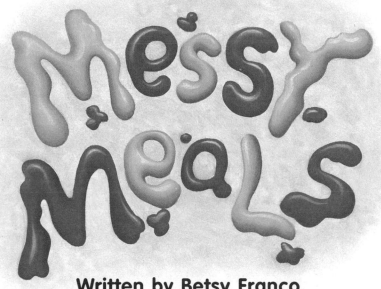

MESSY MEALS

Written by Betsy Franco

Illustrated by Daniel Kirk

SCHOLASTIC INC.

New York Toronto London Auckland Sydney

No part of this publication may be reproduced in whole or in part,
or stored in a retrieval system, or transmitted in any form or by any means,
electronic, mechanical, photocopying, recording, or otherwise, without
written permission of the publisher. For information regarding permission,
write to Scholastic Inc., 555 Broadway, New York, NY 10012.

Copyright © 1994 by Scholastic Inc.
All rights reserved. Published by Scholastic Inc.
Printed in the U.S.A.
ISBN 0-590-27383-3

2 3 4 5 6 7 8 9 10   09   00 99 98 97 96 95 94

4

Eggs on her ears,
Ketchup on her nose,
Crispy warm bacon
Between her toes.

Toast on her tummy,
Jelly on her nose,
Gooey white cream cheese
Between her toes.

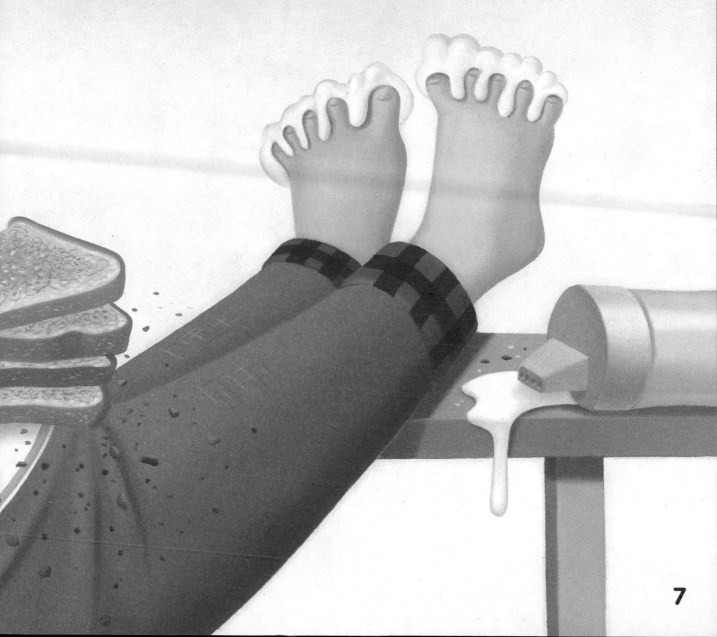

Lettuce on her lap,
Dressing on her nose,
Squishy red tomatoes
Between her toes.

8

Noodles on her knees,
Cheese on her nose,
Little round meatballs
Between her toes.

Chocolate on her chin,
Frosting on her nose,
Cold vanilla ice cream
Between her toes.

What a mess she's made!
Now everybody knows
She loves messy food
Between her toes!